German Panzer II

A VISUAL HISTORY OF THE GERMAN ARMY'S WORLD WAR II LIGHT TANK

by David Doyle

Published by
The Ampersand Group, Inc.
In cooperation with HobbyLink Japan
235 NE 6th Ave., Suite B
Delray Beach, FL 33483-5543
561-266-9686 • 561-266-9786 Fax
www.ampersandpubco.com • www.hlj.com

Acknowledgements:
This book would not have been possible without the generous assistance of the late Walter J. Spielberger. In addition, Jeff Kleinhenz provided invaluable help in the organization and categorization of the many images. Further considerable assistance was provided by Thomas Anderson, Tom Kailbourn, Hans-Heiri Stapfher, Akira Takiguchi, Scott Taylor—and of course my wife Denise who not only scanned hundreds of photographs while we researched this project, but also provided a great deal of support.

All photos credited to "TAG" are copyright of The Ampersand Group, Inc.

Sources:

Achtung Panzer No. 7. Dai Nippon Kaiga Ltd. Tokyo, Japan ISBN 4-499-22773-9.

Panzers I and II and Their Variants by Walther J. Spielberger. Schiffer Publishing, Atglen, PA, 2007 ISBN 978-0-7643-2624-0

Panzer Tracts No. 2-1 Panzerkampfwagen II Ausf. a/1, a/2, a/3, b, c, A, B, and C by Thomas L. Jentz and Hillary L. Doyle. Panzer Tracts, 2008, Boyds, MD. ISBN 0-9815382-2-3.

Panzer Tracts No. 2-2 Panzerkampfwagen II Ausf. G, H, J, L, and M by Thomas L. Jentz and Hillary L. Doyle. Panzer Tracts, 2007, Boyds, MD. ISBN 0-9771643-8-1.

Panzer Tracts No. 2-3 Panzerkampfwagen II Ausf. D, E, and F by Thomas L. Jentz and Hillary L. Doyle. Panzer Tracts, 2010, Boyds, MD.

Panzer Tracts No. 23 Panzer Production from 1944 to 1945 by Thomas L. Jentz and Hillary L. Doyle. Panzer Tracts, 2011, Boyds, MD.

A note on image quality: The historical photographs seen in the Visual History books are always selected from the highest quality original imagery. Images are chosen not only based on their overall clarity, but also for their value in illustrating specific details of the subject vehicle. Our primary sources of images are those held at various government archives, but we also include a small selection of privately owned or purchased photographic prints. Regardless of the source, these images are always prepared at the highest possible resolution—in fact they typically exceed minimum standards for the printing process by a factor of five. The most prominent fact determining image quality is the quality and condition of the original image. Wartime images created by Allied photographers were made with large format cameras, with negatives typically 1/4 the size of the images printed here, although in some cases it is a 1:1 ratio. Those created by German military photographers are almost always shot in the smaller 35mm format. In order to present these as full page requires considerable enlargement. Therefore there will consistently be a noticeable difference between these two groups of photographs. However, the authors strongly feel this does not detract from the significant reference value of these images in print.

Cover: In April 1941, during the Greco-Italian War, Germany invaded Greece, opening a second front to help its Italian ally. Eight days after the Germans entered Greece, a Pz.Kpfw. II drives onto an engineer bridge over a river in that country. A stubby numeral 1 is on the turret, and on the side of the upper hull is an outrigger mount for an antiaircraft machine gun. (NARA)

Back Cover: Four Panzer IIs are among a mixed group of Panzer IVs and Panzer IIIs. This armored group is about to crest a ridge during the opening phases of Operation Barbarossa in June 1941. Groups such as this packed a powerful punch and were essential to the German strategy of rapid exploitation in WWII. (NARA)

Title page: This Pz.Kpfw. II of the Panzer Brigade 4 of the 10th Panzer Division moves forward from the Wadelincourt bridgehead (south of Sedan) towards the Bois de la Marfée on 14 May 1940. The motorcycles to the left are probably from the 10th Schützen Brigade 10. (NARA)

Table of Contents

In this view of a column of Pz.Kpfw. IIs, the blackout taillight is clearly visible below the tailpipe of the closest vehicle, and one is also visible on the second tank. A directive of 21 October 1940 called for the retrofitting of Notek blackout headlights and blackout taillights to Pz.Kpfw. IIs. On the rear deck of the closest tank is a crate and three Jerrycans stowed on their sides. (NARA)

Introduction

Despite the provisions of the Treaty of Versailles, Germany clandestinely embarked on an ambitious rearmament program in the early 1930s. As is well-known, this program, already extensive, greatly increased once Hitler came into power in 1933.

One such program called for the creation of a 6-ton light tank. As with the Panzer I, which was given the code name Kleintraktor, the 6-ton tank was also given a code name that falsely indicated it was agricultural equipment—Landwirtschaftlicher Schlepper 100 (La.S.100)—or farm tractor with 100-horsepower engine.

Initially it was thought that Krupp would be the contractor for this vehicle, and in fact Krupp presented rough chassis designs for the vehicle to the German ordnance department (Waffenamt) on 24 February 1934.

Ordnance, rather than giving Krupp a go-ahead, requested competing proposals for chassis from Henschel and Maschinenfabrik Augsburg-Nürnberg (MAN). Upon review of the proposals, all three firms were contracted to build two trial chassis each. All six of these chassis had been delivered by the end of 1935.

Ultimately the MAN chassis design was selected for production, and it was to be combined with a superstructure and turret designed by Daimler-Benz. An order was placed for 75 of the new tanks in October 1935, with the chassis to be divided into three series of 25 each, which were designated Ausf. a/1, Ausf. a/2 and Ausf. a/3. These 75 chassis were built with hulls of high-nickel armor, which permitted the plate to be thinner than the lesser-quality plate used on later chassis while providing equal protection.

Delivery of these 75 vehicles, which had all pretense of agricultural equipment dropped by the redesignation as Panzerkampfwagen II (referred to hereafter as the Panzer II or Pz.Kpfw. II) on 3 April 1936, was scheduled for April through September 1936.

By June of 1936 the decision had been made to produce an additional 425 vehicles. While the Panzer II was a combat-capable vehicle, and was used as such effectively, especially in the early stages of the war, acquiring the Panzer II for combat was far from the only reason it was placed in production—and why the orders were steadily increased.

As of 30 September 1936 orders had been issued for 460 Panzer II. While initially chassis production was by MAN and superstructure/turret production by Daimler-Benz, by the fourth series, known as the Panzer II Ausf. A, two additional assembly plants had been included. The 460 vehicles were broken into the following series:

Series 1	25 units Ausf. a/1
Series 1	25 units Ausf. a/2
Series 1	25 units Ausf. a/3
Series 2	100 units Ausf. b
Series 2	31 units Ausf. c
Series 3	44 units Ausf. c
Series 4	210 units Ausf. A

Because Germany had been forbidden from producing tanks in the years following WWI, the country lacked the manufacturing—and to a certain extent, the engineering expertise, to mass-produce what at that time were considered heavy tanks, such as the Panzer III and IV. Skills acquired by producing the Panzer II, from the machinist to the assembly worker to the engineer, would translate into greater quality and efficiency in the more expensive, heavier tanks.

Once skilled tradesmen were on a company's payroll, it was important to keep them working. In any manufacturing operation, the overall rate of production is governed by the single component with the lowest rate of production. In order to keep skilled workers on the job, final assembly rates were adjusted—and additional orders placed—so that production was continuous. Germany wanted to keep the Panzer II in production long enough that the skilled work force would be in place when the time came to produce larger tanks.

This situation is not unique to German industry. General Motors and Chrysler used similar methods in the U.S. in order to avoid lay-offs. In the case of the American companies, final assembly rates never reached the maximum capacity of the plant or assembly workers—and in fact fell far short of those quantities—owing to difficulties securing certain components.

Because, as of February 1937 Panzer III engineering and testing were not far enough progressed to permit production before an anticipated initial date of 1 October 1938, it was decided to continue Panzer II production for the reasons enumerated above. These vehicles were covered by contracts for chassis in the 5th, 6th and 7th series.

By Ausführung (Ausf.), these series were divided in this way:

Series 5	326 units Ausf. B
Series 6	58 units Ausf. B
Series 7	364 units Ausf. C

In order that additional companies become familiar with tank production, by this point the chassis manufacturing pool extended beyond MAN to include the firms of Henschel, Mühlenbau-Industrie A.G. (MIAG) and Fahrzeug-und Motoren-Werke (FAMO), among others. Panzer II turrets and superstructures, previously exclusively supplied by Daimler-Benz, began to be produced by Wegmann beginning with the Series 4 vehicles. In time various chassis manufacturers also began to produce superstructures and turrets.

Panzer II Ausf. D

Chief engineer and head of the Waffenamt Prüfwesen 6 Heinrich Ernst Kniepkamp was not notably pleased with the MAN design, in particular its performance, longevity and ease of maintenance. A completely new design was created, which was powered by the Maybach HL 62. The chassis of the new designed was designated the

In 1935, Maschinenfrabrik Augsburg-Nürnberg (MAN) was one of several manufacturers that submitted prototypes for a light tank chassis that would have the capability of mounting a 20mm cannon. The prototypes were produced under the intentionally misleading designation Landwirtschaftlicher Schlepper 100 (La.S. 100: agricultural tractor). The MAN prototype is shown here during cross country trials. It also carried the designation as the VK 622, VK standing for Versuchskraftfahrzeug: experimental vehicle, and the MAN chassis would become the basis for the Pz.Kpfw. II Ausf. a. (Image Bank WW2)

La.S.138, series 8. The vehicles were to be armed with a 2 cm Kw.K.30 cannon and a 7.92mm MG 34.

Orders for four trial and 85 production examples of the new design Panzer II, designated Ausf. D, were placed in 1937, with delivery scheduled from October 1938 through March 1939. The chassis were to be built by MAN and the armor by Deutsche Edelstahlwerke. Only 43 of the tanks had been completed by April 1939 when the contract was changed to specify that the new vehicles be completed as flamethrower tanks (Flammpanzer). Further, on 8 March 1940, the 43 Panzer II Ausf. D tanks that had been issued to troops, primarily Panzer battalions 66 and 67, were ordered to turn these vehicles in so that they too could be converted to flamethrowers. The tanks were shipped to the XI Corps army tank depot (Heerespanzerzeugamt) at Magdeburg-Königsborn.

Panzer II (F) Ausf. A. & B

When rearmed as a flamethrower, the Panzer II Ausf. D was redesignated the Panzerkampfwagen II (Flammenwerferwagen) Ausf. A—often shortened to Panzer II (F), Ausf. A. Wegmann in Kassel was contracted to design the required turret and superstructure, as well as perform the conversions.

The modifications were extensive, with a new turret armed with a ball-mounted MG 34 being installed. Two flame projectors were installed, with one being mounted on top of each front fender. The projectors could be traversed through an arc 45-degrees either side of their centerline. One hundred sixty liters of flamethrower fuel were carried, enough for roughly 80 bursts.

A trial conversion using carbon steel components was completed in July 1939, with series production beginning in January of the following year. However, deficiencies in the flammpanzers brought deliveries to a halt in April, and required the 20 delivered vehicles be returned for further modifications. Deliveries resumed in May 1940. In addition to the 89 vehicles created from the Panzer II Ausf. D on series 8 La.S.138 chassis, a further 62 examples, known as the Ausf. B, were built on newly contracted chassis, interestingly designated the series 2 La.S.138 chassis. Flamethrower-equipped Panzer II production continued until March 1942.

Panzer II Ausf. F

In early 1939 a further 404 Panzer II gun tanks were ordered. These vehicles were to be a new model, introducing improvements such as heavier, 30mm-thick front armor and a cupola with periscopes. The chassis for the new vehicles was designated the La.S.100 series 9. Initial plans were that the production of these vehicles was to be divided between FAMO and Alkett. On 19 September 1940 production of the 200 vehicles previously assigned to Alkett was transferred to Poland's Ursus. By June 1940 plans were underway for a new style Panzer II to enter production, the Panzer II Ausf. H, or VK903. However, it was clear that the design would not be ready for production by the time the 404 Panzer II Ausf. F were completed. In order to keep the production workers busy in the interim, contracts were issued for 600 additional Panzer II Ausf. F.

Ursus began deliveries in March 1941, delivering the final vehicle in July 1942. FAMO production ran from August 1941 through June 1942.

However, senior leaders—including Adolf Hitler and Albert Speer—questioned the utility of the aging Panzer II design. Thus, the decision was made to utilize the bulk of the additional chassis as the basis for the Marder II (Sd.Kfz. 131) open-topped tank destroyer armed with a PaK 40 75mm antitank gun.

Ultimately, Panzer II F gun tank production was broken down like this:

Series 9, Ursus	389 units
Series 9, FAMO	120 units

Panzer II, Ausf. G

Efforts to create a totally new design of Panzer II began in 1938, with MAN contracted for the chassis and Daimler-Benz for the superstructure and turret. Emphasis was placed on high speed and improved protection.

The design agreed upon featured interleaved road wheels, a 150-horsepower Maybach HL 45 engine coupled to an 8-speed transmission giving a to speed of 65 km/h, and was armed with a stabilized 2 cm KwK 38 cannon and 7.92mm MG 34. The chassis was designated as the VK 9.01.

Five operational trial chassis were ordered from MAN, and orders were placed with MAN and Daimler-Benz for 30 production vehicles, which was later upped to 75, with production scheduled from May until October 1940. The final 45 of these were to be built on the VK 9.02 chassis, which were to have improved steering units.

However, as with many of Germany's tank programs, actual production fell far short of these goals. By August 1941 only 15 of the chassis had been delivered, but no turrets or superstructures. In July 1942, perhaps in disgust, or perhaps owing to the need to utilize the production capacity for other purposes, the 75-tank order was cut to 55 units instead. By February 1943 45 of the 55 chassis had been completed by MAN, while Daimler-Benz reported having completed 60 sets of superstructures and turrets by the end of 1942.

Panzer II Ausf. H.

Even though the Panzer II Ausf. G program could not be considered a success by anyone's standards, nevertheless the Waffenamt in June 1940 wanted to further increase the armor protection of the vehicle, yet maintain a high speed. Dutifully, the designers at MAN, already overwhelmed by the demands of the VK901 and Panther programs, began working out the design for the VK903, or Panzer II Ausf. H. As with the Auf. G. program, MAN was contracted to produce five trial chassis, and Daimler-Benz contracted to design the turret and superstructure.

MAN selected the Maybach HL 66 200-horsepower engine for the new vehicle, which was to be coupled with a strengthened transmission taken from the VK901 program. After months of discussions, planning and creating ambitious projections for production—one even mentioning a desire for 2,592 of the vehicles—in March 1942 the project was abandoned in favor of the VK1303.

Panzer II Ausf. J

By 1939 it was apparent that heavier armor would be required in the face of developing Soviet weapons. Accordingly, Daimler-Benz

and MAN were asked to engineer a new version of the Panzer II boasting 80mm frontal armor. The resultant vehicle, based on the VK1601 chassis, would be powered by a Maybach HL 45 150-horsepower engine and feature interleaved road wheels. It would be armed with the 2 cm KwK 38.

Because of the considerable similarity between the VK1601 and the VK1801 (Panzer I, Ausf. F), MAN was directed to collaborate with Krauss-Maffei, contractors for the latter vehicle. MAN was to build four trial VK1601, with Krauss-Maffei supplying the steering gear and final drive components. A mild steel chassis was available for inspection in June 1940.

On 22 December 1939 authorization was given to build 30 of the vehicles, and MAN and Daimler-Benz were contracted accordingly. By August 1941 MAN had completed only three trial chassis, but estimated series production of the vehicles was imminent while simultaneously expressing concern about the lack of turret deliveries. In fact, turret and armor problems continued to be a problem, which along with the slipping priority of this project meant that only eight finished vehicles were completed in 1941, with the remaining 22 of the 30 vehicles on the initial order not being completed until December 1942. Not surprisingly, the follow-on order for 100 additional units was cancelled in July 1942.

The 22 completed vehicles were used sporadically in the Leningrad area as well as in France and Yugoslavia.

Panzerspähwagen II (Sd. Kfz. 123)

Initially known as the Panzerkampfwagen II neu Art (VK 1301), this vehicle was later redesignated as an armored car, rather than a tank, despite retaining its full track-laying design. The considerable resemblance between the new VK1301 and the ill-fated VK901 (Panzer II Ausf. G) was likely owing to their identical parentage—with MAN once again being contracted for the chassis and Daimler-Benz for the turret and superstructure. However, the VK1301 would have a crew of four, while the Panzer II Ausf. G had a three-man crew.

Owing to the vehicle's intended use in reconnaissance, emphasis was placed on off-road mobility and high speed, particularly in reverse. The powerplant was to be the Maybach HL 45 engine developing 150 horsepower. Armament was planned as a 2cm KwK 38 and a coaxially mounted MG 34.

While 15 experimental chassis for the VK1301 were ordered, none had been completed before the decision was made to replace the VK1301 with the VK1303, powered by the 200-horsepower Maybach HL 66 P, yielding a road speed of 60 km/h and 30 km/h cross-country when coupled to the SSG 48 6-speed transmission.

The VK1303, known alternately as the Panzer II Ausf. L or Panzerspähwagen II, was ordered for production well before testing was complete. A flurry of orders and change orders saw the quantities desired climb from 250 to 500 to 800, but by February 1943 the final decision had been made to produce only 100 of the vehicles.

Delivery of these vehicles, popularly known as the Luchs (Lynx, or Bobcat), began by MAN in September 1942, with production extending until January 1944. Initially deployed on the Eastern Front, additional Luchs were deployed in Normandy in the summer of 1944.

Pz.Kpfw. II Ausf. a

The first series of the Pz.Kpfw. II was the Ausführung a (abbreviated as Ausf.), with three sub-models numbered a/1, a/2, and a/3. A total of 75 were produced. A drive sprocket with four bolts on the hub is an identifying feature of an Ausf.a. The bogie wheels were mounted in pairs, with the front wheel of each pair mounted on a shaft and the rear wheel mounted on a leaf spring. This vehicle has the cast-steel idler wheels that replaced the aluminum wheels with rubber tires after the 10th chassis. An inclined trough for housing the pivoting radio antenna when not in use is alongside the upper hull or superstructure. The weapon mounted here is not the normal 2cm KwK 30 cannon. (TAG)

The fully rotating turret of the Pz.Kpfw. II Ausf. a was armed with a 2cm KwK 30 automatic cannon and a 7.92mm MG 34 machine gun, mounted to elevate in unison. Neither gun is installed in this vehicle. The driver had three vision ports: a wide one to his front with no vision slits, and a narrower one to each side, with vision slits backed by protective glass. Pre-production vehicles (Ausf. a-c) are characterized by the wide, plain front flap for the driver. When the front port was open, there was a windshield in the opening to protect the driver from dust and wind. When the front port was closed, the driver saw to the front using a binocular periscope, with sighting holes visible between the hinges of the vision port. Note the presence now of tow-cable holders on the final-drive housing. **Inset:** Both the Ausf. a and b pre-production versions had two fuel fillers on the right superstructure side. These were moved to the roof of the superstructure on the Ausf. c. A vision slit on the right forward turret vision side is also characteristic of an Ausf. a. (TAG, both)

A Pz.Kpfw. II Ausf. a leads a column of Pz.Kpfw. Is through newly renamed Adolf Hitler Square in Chomutov (Komotau in German), Sudetenland, on 9 October 1938. The number 205 is painted on the side of the turret. There is an A-shaped bracket or fitting attached to the roof of the turret to the front of the hatch, reportedly used as an antiaircraft machine gun mount. To the front of that fitting is a dummy periscope, intended to draw enemy gunners' attention away from the sight apertures in the mantlet. Note the nonslip tread pattern on the fenders. (BA 146-2006-0020)

In a view of the rear of a Pz.Kpfw. II Ausf. a, below the tailpipe is the taillight assembly. Below the muffler is the engine-starter crank. On the left fender is a jack. To the rear of the head of the man to the left is the access cover for mounting the fan belts. Marked on the rear plate of the radio operator's compartment on the left side of the upper hull is a rhomboidal symbol of a panzer unit, with the number 1 to its lower right. A two-colored band has been stretched around the top of the turret. These are pre-war markings. (Thomas Anderson)

Pz.Kpfw. II Ausf. a tanks of Panzer Regiment 1 are crossing a bridge over the Saône River in France on 15 June 40. What appear to be sunscreens have been installed above the driver's forward vision ports on the two vehicles that are totally visible. On the nearest tank, spare track sections are on the front deck and across the front of the final drive housing All-around armor thickness on the Ausf. a was 13mm, with 15mm on the mantlet. It was intended for proof against 7.92mm rounds. (NARA)

Left: In a view of the rear of a Pz.Kpfw. II Ausf. a during the Polish Campaign, the distinctive round cooling-fan grille on the left rear corner of the rear deck is visible, along with the muffler and tailpipe. Inboard of the left idler wheel is a reinforcing cone that was retrofitted to some examples of the Pz.Kpfw. II Ausf. a. These added strength to the rear of the chassis. Mounted on the muffler is a Nebelkerzenabwurfvorrichtung (N.K.A.V.), a device that contained five smoke canisters that could be dropped to the rear of the vehicle to lay down a smokescreen. (Akira Takiguchi) **Right:** Apparently newly-minted Pz.Kpfw. IIs without any visible markings are loaded on flatcars at a railroad station. The Ausf. a and Ausf. b both used a 130 hp Maybach HL 57 TR engine coupled to a Z.F. S.S.G.45 six-speed transmission. Top speed was 40 km/h. Road range was 190 km and cross-country range was 126 km. (Thomas Anderson)

Pz.Kpfw. II Ausf. b

The Pz.Kpfw. II Ausf. b, of which 100 were produced, was an improved version of the Ausf. a vehicles and included a redesigned bow to accommodate a new steering mechanism. The use of rolled, homogenous, nickel-free armor; new sprockets; and a drastically redesigned rear deck. The nickel-free armor thickness was increased to 14.5mm all around, with 16mm on the mantlet. This was standard through to the Ausf. C. On the side of the upper hull next to the turret is an Auslegearm für Flugabwehr (outrigger mount for an antiaircraft machine gun), for supporting an MG 34 to be operated by a gunner on the ground next to the tank. This arm was mounted on Ausf. b and c pre-production models and Ausf. A and Ausf. B vehicles until discontinued in 1938. (TAG)

A Pz.Kpfw. II Ausf. b is parked on a plaza in an unidentified city. The vehicle exhibits the plain, flat, driver's right vision port and the similar vision port on the left side of the turret that were hallmarks of the Ausf. b. To the front of the driver's front vision port is the driver's door. A fire extinguisher is visible to the right side of the superstructure, a pre-production feature when two were equipped. The other was located beside the jack on the left rear fender. (Hans-Heiri Stapfer)

Three Pz.Kpfw. IIs of the 3rd Panzer Regiment are lined up next to an Sd.Kfz. 265 Kleine Befehlswagen, a communications vehicle based on the Pz.Kpfw. I, to the far right, at a repair depot in Brno, Czechoslovakia, on 22 March 1939. The center Pz.Kpfw. II is an Ausf. b, with the smooth vision ports to the driver's front and right. The vehicles to the left and the right of that tank are either Ausf. A or early Ausf. Bs, judging by the styles of the vision ports and the presence of splashguards around the turrets, a feature introduced during Ausf. A production. (NARA)

The same group of vehicles seen in the preceding photo is viewed from the opposite direction. The vehicle with the soldiers standing on it toward the right is a Pz.Kpfw. II Ausf. b. This vehicle has a distinctive right side of the rear deck, in which the rear of the engine cover ends above the level of the deck. The hood is wider than the cooling-air exhaust grille to the immediate rear of it, resulting in a pronounced, L-shaped recess. This feature is more apparent when compared to the engine cover on the vehicle to the left of it, a Pz.Kpfw. II of the Ausf. A through C model range. (NARA)

Among an array of 3rd Panzer Regiment Pz.Kpfw. Is and IIs and other vehicles at a depot in Brno, Czechoslovakia, on 22 March 1939 is a Pz.Kpfw. II Ausf. b in the right foreground. It is distinguished from an Ausf. a by its redesigned drive sprocket and the presence of a flat visor with no vision slit on the left rear of the turret. (NARA)

Two Pz.Kpfw. IIs in the foreground are part of a road march involving several other types of tanks during the French campaign. The closest vehicle is a Pz.Kpfw. II Ausf. b, as evidenced by its six-bogie-wheel suspension, the revised drive sprocket, and the shapes of the muffler and the left side of the rear of the hull. Both Pz.Kpfw. IIs have the N.K.A.V. smoke-grenade racks on the mufflers. (BA 127-0396-13A)

This example of a Pz.Kpfw. II Ausf. b, chassis number 21022, was the 22nd of 100 produced. It exhibits only one readily noticeable modification: the addition of a Notek blackout light to the right of the left headlight. This addition was instituted in October 1940. Both the Ausf. a and Ausf. b had problems with wear on the small wheels, thus the switch to the larger wheels that would become standard with the Ausf. c. (Thomas Anderson)

Some of the Pz.Kpfw. II Ausf. b tanks participated in the 1941 invasion of the Soviet Union. This example is towing a small trailer with a barrel. On the left rear fender is a triple smoke discharger. To the rear of the Balkenkreuz on the hull is the symbol for the 12th Panzer Division. The code A96 stands for Aufklärungs (Reconnaissance Battalion), 9th Platoon, 6th vehicle. Note the two spare roadwheels, held in place with spare tracks, on the glacis. (BA 265-0003-14A)

Pz.Kpfw. II Ausf. c and A-C early

The Ausf.c introduced the suspension with five large roadwheels and a leaf-spring suspension that would become standard for the Panzer II through to the Ausf. F. The engine was also upgraded. The original Maybach HL 57 TR had its cylinders bored out to become the 140 hp HL 62 TR. Overall automotive performance was unchanged. This tank belongs to the 1st Company of Panzer Regiment 25 of the 7th Panzer Division. It is seen passing through a French border crossing on May 16th 1940. (NARA)

In a somewhat grainy view of a German armored column crossing a highway bridge, the lead vehicle is a Pz.Kpfw. II Ausf. c, as indicated by the large, flat front vision port for the driver, and the driver's right vision port, which is flat, with no vision slit. Also note the lack of a turret splashguard on the superstructure roof. (BA 116-483-015)

This Pz.Kpfw. II that has become bogged in a marsh has the driver's front vision port of an Ausf. A to C that was smaller, had a triangular profile and a small vision slit. The driver's right vision port is that of a late Ausf. B or an Ausf. C, with two bolts below the vision slit and two bolts above and two bolts below the port. This modification came about due to the addition of a 50mm glass block being added to protect against bullets entering the vision slit. (NARA)

This photograph of soldiers inspecting Pz.Kpfw. IIs of the 3rd Panzer Regiment at a repair depot in Brno, Czechoslovakia, on 22 March 1939 are part of a series showing these specific vehicles and several others from various angles. Thus, it is possible to determine these tank's approximate Ausführung designations. The nearest tank is a Pz.Kpfw. II Ausf. b, while the next vehicle is a Pz.Kpfw. IIs Ausf. A, B, or C. Next are a Pz.Kpfw. III and several trucks. (NARA)

The same two Pz.Kpfw. IIs and Pz.Kpfw. III seen in the preceding photo are seen from another perspective, with the addition at the far right of another Pz.Kpfw. II, an Ausf. A or early Ausf. B, based on the styles of the various vision ports. The splashguard on the superstructure roof was introduced during Ausf. A production to prevent bullets jamming the turret race. (NARA)

A Pz.Kpfw. II photographed during a parade in Czechoslovakia exhibits on its turret a rear vision port and a rear side vision port characteristic of a late Ausf. B or C machine, with two bolts below the vision slits, two bolts above and two bolts below the ports. This vehicle has the reinforcing rod between the idler mounts across the rear of the hull. Note the lifting eyes at the upper rear corners of the hull. (NARA)

Two Pz.Kpfw. IIs pass by a sign in the Czech language. The closer one has attributes of an Ausf. c, Ausf. A, or early Ausf. B vehicle, such as a split hatch on the turret, the style of vision ports and wheels, and the lack of fuel-filler ports on the side of the upper hull. On the muffler is an N.K.A.V. smoke-grenade rack. (NARA)

Tank transporters are loaded with light tanks at a site in Czechoslovakia. The closest Pz.Kpfw. II has a split hatch, and the driver's right vision port is of the style found on the late Ausf. B and the Ausf. C, with two bolts below the vision slit. A jacket is draped over the 20mm cannon barrel. (NARA)

This Pz.Kpfw. II loaded on a tank-transporter trailer could be anything from an Ausf. c to an Ausf. B, based on the style of the rear vision port on the turret, with two bolts above the vision slit and one bolt below it. The two-meter radio antenna has been lowered into its protective trough. Stored on the fender are a fire extinguisher, a jack, and a wooden jack block. (TAG)

A column of Pz.Kpfw. IIs pass through a border checkpoint during operations in the winter. The closest vehicle provides a rare view of one of these tanks with the radio-operator's hatch open; the radio operator is sitting in the open hatch to the front of the louvered hatch door. The single-panel door with enlarged louvers for engine-cooling was introduced with the Ausf. A, replacing the earlier split doors. This is a late-production Ausf. B or Ausf. C. (NARA)

A column of Pz.Kpfw. IIs parades down a street in Wenceslas Square in Prague, Czechoslovakia, on 20 April 1939. The closest tank has a rhomboid placard on the rear identifying it as a 2nd Battalion staff vehicle. Reinforcing rods are present on the rears of the hulls of at least the first two vehicles. As far as can be determined, these vehicles were consistent with Ausf. c through early Ausf. B tanks. (IWM)

Tool stowage on the left fender would remain fairly standard throughout Pz.Kpfw. II production with the jack, jack block and fire extinguisher to the rear of the trough for the folding antenna. A large crowbar was stowed under this trough and a shovel was located inside and forward of the trough. (TAG)

Of these two Pz.Kpfw. IIs photographed in Poland in 1939, the closer vehicle has the type of front driver's hatch associated with Ausf. A to C. Both vehicles have the pedestal mounts for antiaircraft machine guns to the fronts of the split hatches of the turrets. A swastika pennant is hanging under the right hatch door. Equipment racks are on the fenders of both tanks; the one on the closer tank is loaded with three Jerrycans. Note that most of the white crosses on the turrets have been painted over, filled with yellow paint. (BA 012-0022-23)

The crew of a Pz.Kpfw. II of the 5th Panzer Division prepare to replace a track during the initial days of the invasion of Poland in early September 1939. The vehicle is marked with yellow identification crosses. Below the number 12 on the turret is a rhomboidal symbol painted yellow, black, and yellow, that was intended to mark vehicles of the 15th Panzer Regiment. The presence of splash guards on the hull roof and the style of the vision ports are consistent with an Ausf. A or early Ausf. B vehicle. Note the reinforcing rod across the rear of the hull below the tow coupling: a modification implemented in 1938 and 1939. (NARA)

Left: A man with a brush in his left hand and a sprayer in the other applies paint to the upper hull of a Pz.Kpfw. II. Based on the style of bogie wheel and the rear vision port on the turret with two bolts above the vision slit and one bolt below it, this vehicle could be in the range of Ausf. c, A, or B. The Pz.Kpfw. II in the background has a reinforcing rod across the rear of the hull just below the tow coupling: a feature found on Ausf. C vehicles but also a modification performed on Ausf. c, A, and B vehicles. The sign on the side of the truck in the background makes reference to the 2nd Battalion, 1st Panzer Regiment. (Hans-Heiri Stapfer)

Right: This photograph of a Pz.Kpfw. II emerging from the water affords a rare view of the rear deck, unencumbered with stowed equipment. On the engine-access doors is a white rectangle: the air-recognition symbol used on these tanks from late 1939 through the Western campaigns of 1940. The radio-operator's hatch on the left front of the deck has the single-panel door introduced with the Ausf. A. The arrangement of the bolts on the radio-operator's vision port is in keeping with Ausf. A or early Ausf. B. Note the raised rim around the perimeter of the turret hatch. (TAG)

Wehrmacht vehicles assembled in a field include three Pz.Kpfw. IIs in the column to the left and one at the front of the column to the right. The drivers' doors are open, and the drivers' front vision ports of the two vehicles in the front row are of the type of the Ausf. A to Ausf. C. (NARA)

A Pz.Kpfw. II Ausf. B leads a column during the 1939 Poland campaign and is followed by two Pz.Kpfw. Is, another Pz.Kpfw. II, and two Kleine Panzerbefehlswagen. The splashguards on the driver's side vision ports were introduced with the Ausf. B. All of the vehicles except the Pz.Kpfw. Is have white identification crosses painted on the fronts of the turrets or, in the case of the Kleine Panzerbefehlswagen, on the glacis: a widespread practice during the invasion of Poland. (NARA)

Panzerkampfwagen Is (rear) and three Pz.Kpfw. IIs with Ausf. A or early Ausf. B vision ports pass by during the 5 October 1939 victory parade in Warsaw, Poland, attended by Adolf Hitler. During the Poland campaign, experience proved that the white identification crosses on vehicles were a glaring target for enemy gunners, so the Panzer crews fixed the problem by overpainting the crosses with a yellowish paint. The two Pz.Kpfw. IIs to the right appear to have crosses that received that toning-down treatment. (NARA)

A Wehrmacht soldier motions forward the driver of a Pz.Kpfw. II as the tank crosses a ditch via a bridge improvised from logs. This vehicle exhibits attributes of an Ausf. B machine, with three bolts on the driver's side vision ports and the bullet splashguard in front. A number, 306, is on a rhomboid plate on the side of the upper hull. (BA 123-0177-16A)

The same Pz.Kpfw. II shown in the preceding photograph is viewed from another angle as it proceeds across a log bridge. The symbol of the 6th Panzer Division as used in 1940, an inverted Y with two dots to the right of it, is on the outboard side of the driver's frontal armor. (NARA)

Here is another 6th Panzer Division vehicle. This was a late Ausf. B or an early Ausf. C example, as indicated by the presence, though faintly visible, of bullet deflectors to the front of the driver's side vision ports. (BA 123-0180-34A)

Civilians, including some children, get an opportunity to view a row of Pz.Kpfw. IIs close-up in an unidentified city. The nearest vehicle is an Ausf. a, as evidenced by the four-bolt drive sprocket. This tank has the number 243 roughly painted on the driver's frontal armor. The second vehicle has driver's vision ports consistent with an Ausf. A or B vehicle. (Image Bank WW2)

A Pz.Kpfw. II with splash guards on the hull roof and the driver's front vision port of the Ausf. A to C types precedes a Pz.Kpfw. I during a wintertime operation. Very faintly visible on the upper-outboard corner of the driver's frontal armor is the symbol of the 7th Panzer Division as it appeared in 1940: an inverted Y with three dots to its right side. (NARA)

Several indicators of the Ausfürung type of this Pz.Kpfw. II are readily apparent. The slightly raised feature to the front of the driver's side vision port is a splashguard, introduced during Ausf. B production. The turret and driver's right vision ports are in the style of late Ausf. B and Ausf. C vehicles, with two bolts below the vision slit, two bolts above the port, and two more bolts below the port. The purpose of the bolts above and below the port were to secure 50mm-thick shatterproof glass blocks, introduced during Ausf. B production. (TAG)

Crewmen of a Pz.Kpfw. II pause for a meal during the advance just west of Cambrai, France, on 23 May 1940. The driver's front and right vision ports are in the style of Ausf. b or c. To the side of the front vision port is the symbol of the 4th Panzer Division. (NARA)

An insignia is visible is barely visible in front of the crewman seated on the rear deck: the letter "K" of Gruppe von Kleist. The white crosses are also indicative of units attached to this Gruppe. This vehicle is part of the group of tanks of the 2nd Panzer Division photographed crossing into Luxembourg during the first week of May 1940. The visible features indicate that this is an Ausf. B or C. (NARA)

This Pz.Kpfw. II Ausf A was photographed while crashing through a brick building. A clear view is available of the split legs that supported the trough for storing the radio antenna in the lowered position. The large crowbar stowed underneath the trough can be seen clearly here. Note the prewar tactical symbol to the left of the radio-operator's vision port and that neither the main gun nor the coaxial MG 34 is fitted to this vehicle. (TAG)

This vehicle is a Pz.Kpfw. II Ausf. A judging from the bullet splashguard on the superstructure roof and bolt arrangement on the driver's left side vision port. On the side of the turret is the tactical symbol for corps headquarters. Note the Italian CV-33 light tank to the left. (TAG)

A Pz.Kpfw. II churns up dust during an exercise. The tank is marked with the vehicle number 143 above the Fliegerauslegerarm machine gun outrigger mount on the side of the hull. From sparse details available, this tank was in the model range of Ausf. c to early Ausf. B. (NARA)

The driver's small front vision port, the three-bolt side vision ports with vision slits, the presence of splash guards on the hull roof and lack of bullet deflectors in front of the driver's left and right side vision ports indicate that this Pz.Kpfw. II is an Ausf. A. (Patton Museum)

Panzerkampfwagen IIs were present for the April 1940 invasion of Norway and the subsequent occupation of that country. Here, an infantryman slogs along next to a Pz.Kpfw. II in the Ausf. c to Ausf. B range. The vehicle was assigned to Panzer-Abteilung z.b.V.40 (z.b.V. stood for *zur besonderen Verwendung*: for special utilization). Part of a smoke-grenade rack is visible on the muffler shield. (NARA).

The commander of a Pz.Kpfw. II Ausf. B or C of Panzer-Abteilung z.b.V. 40 is rapping the hull with a hammer during an operation in Norway in 1940. A bullet deflector is clearly visible to the front of the driver's right vision port. To the rear of the *Balkenkreuz* is the barely discernible insignia of z.b.V. 40: a V inside a circle. (NARA)

A Pz.Kpfw. II of the 36th Panzer Regiment, 4th Panzer Division, advances through a gap in a stone wall outside of Maastricht, Belgium, during the battle for that city on 10 May 1940. The markings on the turret signify the vehicle as that of the signals officer, 1st Battalion. On the left side of the rear plate of the turret is the symbol of the 4th Panzer Division. This photo reveals many interesting details of the rear deck and stowage. (BA RH 82 Bild-00090)

The commander of a Pz.Kpfw. II scans the terrain ahead during the advance through Belgium on 13 May 1940. A metal stowage rack for Jerrycans, ammunition boxes or other materials is on the fender. This was a fairly common modification. (NARA)

Pz.Kpfw. II Ausf. c, A, B, C modified

An up-armored Pz.Kpfw. II of the 2nd Panzer Division passes a stone building in Sugny, France, en route to Sedan in May 1940. The tank bears markings on the hull for Signals officer, 2nd Battalion, of the respective regiment. Note the two-part painting of the Balkenkreuz: the upper half is on the hull, and the lower half is on the antenna trough and its center support. The Panzer II underwent an armor upgrade program in 1939 following the Polish Campaign. Bolted plates of 20mm thickness were added to the turret face, the driver's glacis plates and the bow plate. The nearly horizontal glacis received a 15mm thick plate. (NARA)

At a crossing of the Maas River, a Pz.Kpfw. II drives onto an engineer bridge. On the deck over the engine compartment, a German flag has been secured as an air-identification aid. On the muffler is a smoke-grenade rack. Faint Balkenkreuzen are visible on the side of the hull and the rear of the radio-operator's compartment, to the left rear of the turret. The additional 20mm turret armor is faintly visible. (NARA)

At a repair shop in Belgium on 20 May 1940, German soldiers work on the right track of a Pz.Kpfw. II retrofitted with supplemental armor. The driver's right visor is the style associated with Ausf. B and C vehicles fitted with the supplemental armor kit: two bolts below the vision slit. The side visors on the supplemental armor were larger than on unmodified tanks. Fabric covers are over the two gun barrels. (NARA)

During the Blitzkrieg in Western Europe in the spring of 1940, a Pz.Kpfw. II of the 6th Company, 2nd Battalion, 3rd Panzer Regiment, 2nd Panzer Division, leads a Pz.Kpfw. I along a forest road. The marking "RO2" on the hull indicates the vehicle of the regimental executive officer. The supplemental armor package was installed on some but not all Panzer IIs, as seen in previous pictures from the 4th Panzer Division in the 1940 Campaign. (BA 382-0248-33A)

Three French soldiers are on the rear of a Pz.Kpfw. II during the German Blitzkrieg in the spring of 1940. Although this vehicle is in the Ausf. c to Ausf. C range, it has the hinged rear mud flaps that were introduced with the Pz.Kpfw. II Ausf. b. Note the battered, perforated shield on the muffler. (Image Bank WW2)

A column of Pz.Kpfw. II of the 5th Panzer Division progresses through the town of Forge-à-l'Aplé on 12 May 1940. The hinged frame for mounting a machine gun can be seen on the right front fender of the lead vehicle. (NARA)

Details of the interior of the driver's hatch with its cross-shaped, four-bolt locking assembly are available in this photo of a knocked-out Pz.Kpfw. II Ausf. A, B, or C. During the conflagration when the vehicle was destroyed, the rubber tires burned off the bogie wheels and track-support rollers. (TAG)

On the supplemental armor on the front of the driver's compartment of this Pz.Kpfw. II Ausf. A or B is a letter G, signifying a vehicle attached to Panzergruppe Guderian, commanded by Gen. Heinz W. Guderian during the invasion of France. The construction of the supplemental armor on the front of the hull, particularly the filler piece on the side, is illustrated. There appears to be a drawing on the turret side immediately in front of the flag that is draped on the turret. (TAG)

The Y symbol on the side of the upper hull of this Pz.Kpfw. II Ausf. A or B was the one the 7th Panzer Division adopted in the latter part of 1940. The three bolt heads on the right driver side vision port are indicative of an up-armored Ausf. A or B. The storage box with the Balkenkreuz appears to be of wooden-slat construction. The long box on the rear fender was for spare 2cm barrels. Note the open vision port above the MG 34 barrel. (TAG)

This is another picture from the same sequence as the previous page. This picture provides a good close-up look at the conical bolt heads used for the applique armor, the horn and the lifting hooks on the turret and superstructure roof. (NARA)

An up-armored Pz.Kpfw. II at an assembly area features a Notek blackout headlight on the glacis, adjacent to the left headlight. Notek headlights were authorized for retrofitting on Pz.Kpfw. IIs in October 1940. Although the Notek light hides the driver's front vision port, the hinges of the port are below the two holes for the driver's binocular periscope. This fact combined with the arrangement of bolts on the driver's left vision port (two bolts above the vision slit and one below it) indicate that this was a Pz.Kpfw. II Ausf A or B. (TAG)

A Pz.Kpfw. II is on the advance, followed by an Sd.Kfz. 265 Kleine Befehlswagen. The driver's front vision ports are consistent with an Ausf. B or C. To each side of the aperture is a slot for the operating arms of the driver's front vision port, which also are visible in this photo. The conical bolt arrangement on the supplemental armor is also very clear. (TAG)

A Pz.Kpfw. II Ausf. B or C of the 7th Panzer Division with markings for a regimental staff vehicle on the side of the turret crosses a pontoon bridge near Cuinchy on 27 May 1940. Another Pz.Kpfw. II is trailing behind it. The muzzles of the 20mm and 7.92mm guns have been covered to keep out dust and moisture. The trough for the antenna when lowered has been removed from the front vehicle. (NARA)

The commander of a Pz.Kpfw. II Ausf B or C adjusts his headphones as his tank and the following Pz.Kpfw. II negotiate a narrow spot in the road. The driver side vision port has two bolts below the slit, an indication of an Ausf. B or C. Tool storage on the right forward fender included a crowbar and wire cutters. Behind the fender support can be seen the engine starter crank and the S-shaped tow shackles. (Patton Museum)

A Pz.Kpfw. II of the 7th Panzer Division is embarking on a raft composed of an engineer bridge section on pontoons prior to being ferried across a river during one of the 1940 campaigns. The "I11" marking on the turret indicates that this was a 1st Battalion staff vehicle. In addition to the black and white crosses on the upper hull, there are two placards on the antenna trough, one with a black and white cross and the other with the vehicle number, I11, faintly marked on it. (NARA)

The oak-leaf insignia of the 1st Panzer Division is on the top rear of the turrets of these two Pz.Kpfw. IIs parked in a village in Belgium on 12 May 1940. The vehicle at the center has a blackout taillight below the tailpipe. The vehicle to the left has reinforcing cones on the lower part of the rear plate of the hull, and a smoke-grenade rack on the muffler. The differences in markings on the turret rears of the two Pz.Kpfw. IIs is noteworthy: the vehicle on the left has a large Balkenkreuz on the turret rear with the divisional insignia to the upper right, while the vehicle in the center has the divisional insignia centered above the rear vision slit and the vehicle number, 201, on the lower left of the turret rear. (NARA)

A Pz.Kpfw. II Ausf. A or B is followed by a Pz.Kpfw. II Ausf. a during a road march. Both tanks have outrigger mounts for antiaircraft machine guns on the sides of the upper hulls. A sun shield or rain deflector has been installed above the driver's front vision port on the closer tank. (NARA)

Left: The style of the driver's front and left vision ports are consistent with a Pz.Kpfw. Ausf. A or B. In addition to the front splashguard added to the hull roof to the front of the turret during Ausf. A production, there also was a splashguard at the rear of the turret, and the left end of this feature is visible below the leg of the reclining crewman. A section of three track links is attached to the front of the driver's compartment. This vehicle was assigned to a 2nd Battalion staff officer, as indicated by the Roman numeral II on the turret. Note the place-ment of the Balkenkreuz over the driver's left vision port. (TAG) **Right:** Soldiers of the 1st Panzer Division are taking advantage of warm weather and an available canal to scrub their tanks. The closest Pz.Kpfw. II, with the number 802 on the turret, was likely an Ausf. c, with supplemental armor on the hull and turret, and with a flat plate with no vision slit attached with two bolts to the existing driver's right port. The Pz.Kpfw. II behind the first one is an Ausf. A, B, or C, with a 1st Panzer Division insignia on the turret front. (NARA)

Two French soldiers ham it up for the photographer on the rear of a Pz.Kpfw. II Ausf. A, B, or C of the 3rd Panzer Division. The number 511 is marked on the side of the turret. A large storage box with a padlock on the rear is mounted on spacers on the left side of the rear deck. To the left of the box are a jack and a fire extinguisher. (NARA)

Panzerkampfwagen IIs accompany two Czech-built Pz.Kpfw. 35(t) light tanks and a motor-cycle crew in the background during an advance across a field. Each of the tanks has a swastika recognition flag on the rear deck. Note the storage of Jerrycans on the fenders and rear decks of the Pz.Kpfw. IIs. (NARA)

A Panzer trooper of the 5th Panzer Division inspects the tailpipe of a Pz.Kpfw. II Ausf. B or C while parked across from the Rouen cathedral in northwestern France on 9 June 1940. This photo is often mistakenly placed in Paris, no doubt due to the cathedral's proper name: "Cathédrale *Notre-Dame* de Rouen." A stowage box is mounted on the fender adjacent to the rear of the upper hull, and a section of spare track is on the rear deck. (NARA)

An armored column that includes, front to rear, a Pz.Kpfw. II, a Kleine Befehlswagen, and a Pz.Kpfw. III pauses during a road march. These vehicles are thought to have been assigned to Regiment General Göring and that the "O" markings on the vehicles were that regiment's symbols for staff vehicles. This up-armored Pz.Kpfw. II has left and right driver's vision ports consistent with those of an Ausf. A or B vehicle. (NARA)

In October 1940, a program to retrofit the Panzer II with a cupola was initiated. At the same time, a switch from the troublesome dual-drum magazines to belted ammunition was implemented for the MG 34. Notek lights were also to be fitted at this time. Vehicles with these modifications first saw action in the 1941 Balkans Campaign. Eight days after the Germans entered Greece, a Pz.Kpfw. II drives onto an engineer bridge over a river in that country. A stubby numeral 1 is on the turret, and on the side of the upper hull is an outrigger mount for an antiaircraft machine gun. The front end of the fender is crumpled upward. (NARA)

Several Pz.Kpfw. IIs and two motorcycles roll past the photographer along a road near Tembi Pass on 18 April 1941. An oil can and a mess kit are to the rear of the storage box on the fender next to the turret. A marking in white, R04, is on the side of the hull below the turret, indicating a regimental staff vehicle. (NARA)

This Pz.Kpfw. II with a cupola, supplemental armor, and Ausf. A-to-C-style driver's front vision port was photographed in the same general area as the preceding photo on 18 April 1941. The wedge-shaped object on the fender is an oil can. (NARA)

In a final shot in the series taken near Tembi Pass on 18 April 1941, the rear of the Pz.Kpfw. II marked "R03" is shown. Stowed on the rear deck are three Jerrycans (one is below and to the rear of the crewman), two spare bogie wheels, and a pile of equipment covered by a tarpaulin and a German flag used for aerial recognition. (NARA)

An armored column of the 11th Panzer Division, including two Pz.Kpfw. IIs at the center and the left, advance along a road in Greece in or around April 1941. The tank to the right is marked with the number 42 on the side and rear of the turret. On the left side of the rear of the upper hull is the symbol of the 11th Panzer Division, a circle with a horizontal line through it. Although barely discernible, that symbol is repeated on the side of the upper hull to the rear of the Balkenkreuz, along with the alternate symbol of the 11th Panzer Division, a depiction of a ghost waving a sword. (NARA)

In the foreground in this view of an armored convoy in Greece in April 1941 is a Pz.Kpfw. II Ausf. B or C. Slightly to the rear of that insignia is the other symbol of the 11th Panzer Division at that time: a circle with a vertical line through it. (NARA)

On 12 February 1941 Gen. Erwin Rommel arrived in Tripoli, Libya, and established headquarters for the Deutsches Afrika-Korps. Materiel, including armor, soon began arriving at that port, including this Pz.Kpfw. II photographed along the docks in Tripoli in February 1941. (NARA)

A sometimes-seen modification to early Pz.Kpfw. IIs is the pair of bullet deflectors on the mantlet of this vehicle photographed in North Africa. Like most Pz.Kpfw. IIs by this period, the vehicle has the supplemental armor package, a turret cupola, and a Notek blackout headlight. A British Dingo Scout Car is in the background. (IWM)

In a closely ordered column of Pz.Kpfw. IIs, the first vehicle bears the symbol of the 3rd Panzer Division to the rear of the Balkenkreuz on the hull: an inverted Y with two vertical bars to the right of it. The driver's left vision port on this tank is in the style of the Pz.Kpfw. II Ausf. A and B, but this vehicle can be narrowed down to an Ausf. B by the bullet deflector immediately to the front of the vision port, a feature introduced during Ausf. B production. The mantlets of these tanks have bullet deflectors. (Image Bank WW2)

This disabled or destroyed Pz.Kpfw. II Ausf. A has a severely buckled fender, and all but the front two bogie wheels have lost their rubber tires. It is not clear if the dark spot on the front plate of the hull is a hole from a projectile or a smudge. The Afrika Korps insignia is on the left supplemental armor on the turret, and a badly faded Balkenkreuz is on the side of the turret. (NARA)

Extra radio equipment, including two additional antennae on the right side of the vehicle, was installed in this Pz.Kpfw. II of the Ausf. A to C range, during operations in the North African desert. The forward antenna's base unit is bolted to the front of the storage box on the fender. A funnel is stowed on the turret roof. (TAG)

The same Pz.Kpfw II seen in the preceding photo was photographed from a slightly different angle. The barrels of the MG 34 and the 20mm cannon are covered to keep out dust. (TAG)

This Pz.Kpfw. II Ausf. B or C has the appearance of an abandoned vehicle, with the stowage-box doors open, damaged equipment and litter lying around the tank and the MG 34 having been dismounted. Faintly visible on the left side of the driver's front vision port is the insignia of the 15th Panzer Division, marked on a dark circle in a contrasting color. (NARA)

This Pz.Kpfw. II Ausf. A, B, or C of the 8th Company, 15th Panzer Division, photographed in North Africa in April 1941, was being used as an artillery observation vehicle. On the driver's front plate and the side of the turret is the palm tree and swastika symbol of the Afrika Korps. To the front of the 8 on the turret is the symbol of the 15th Panzer Division: a triangle with a vertical line through it. Two layers of spare track links are on the front of the glacis, with a retainer bar fastened to each fender. (BA 783-0110-12)

German forces advancing across the desert include two Pz.Kpfw. IIs in the Ausf. A to C range at the center and the left. The lead tank has the number 8 on the turret, a stowage box with two lids on the center of the fender, and a bundle of sticks on the rear of the vehicle. The lead vehicle in this photo is the same vehicle shown on the previous page. (Patton Museum)

A German soldier surveys a Pz.Kpfw. II Ausf. A or B with badly deteriorated paint. Bullet deflectors are present on the mantlet, and the driver's left vision port is one that was appropriate for an Ausf. A or B vehicle. (NARA)

In the foreground are two Pz.Kpfw. IIs. The one to the right has the driver's front vision port of an Ausf. A to C vehicle. Black and white identification crosses are present. On the Pz.Kpfw. II to the right, the number 134 is painted to the rear of the cross, and a large storage chest is on the rear of the hull. In the background, soldiers are bathing in a canal, and a long truck convoy is approaching on a road. (NARA)

A Wehrmacht infantryman watches as an up-armored Pz.Kpfw. II Ausf. A or early Ausf. B approaches during the invasion of the Baltic States of the Soviet Union in the summer of 1941. A rain deflector or sun shield is above the driver's front vision port, and the driver's right vision port has a very unorthodox arrangement of bolts, with one above and to the rear of the vision slit and one to the lower front of the slit. (BA 209-0056-19}

A conference is underway around a Pz.Kpfw. II of the 8th Panzer Division. The suspension and the rear vision port on the turret are appropriate for Ausf. c, A, and early B vehicles. The large stowage box was authorized for retrofitting on Ausf. A to C vehicles in May 1941, but no mention was made of Ausf. c vehicles. Thus, this vehicle probably was an Ausf. A or early Ausf. B. (BA 208-24-3A)

The commander of a Pz.Kpfw. II Ausf. A or early Ausf. B fitted with the supplemental armor kit warily scans the terrain ahead as the tank rolls through a settlement in the Soviet Union during Operation Barbarossa in the early summer of 1941. A Notek blackout headlight is mounted on the left fender inboard of the service headlight. A spare bogie wheel and two layers of spare-track sections are secured to the glacis. (BA 265-0003-18A)

This Pz.Kpfw. II bears very faint markings in white paint on the forward part of the side of the turret: "II 10," indicating a 2nd Battalion staff vehicle. Most of the trough for storing the antenna in the lowered position is missing: even the legs. Only the forward part of the trough is present, lying on the fender. Track pins are tucked behind the trough. (TAG)

This picture was taken during Operation Barbarossa in 1941. In the foreground is an up-armored, cupola-equipped Pz.Kpfw. II with the characteristics of an Ausf. A or early Ausf. B vehicle. A tanker's jacket is hanging from the 20mm barrel. The driver's door is open, and a wrecking bar is leaning against the bow. In the background is an array of light tanks of various types, including Pz.Kpfw. II (Flamm)s and Pz.Kpfw. 38(t)s. (Hans-Heiri Stapfer)

In a column parked on a road, awaiting the command to advance, to the right is a Pz.Kpfw. II Ausf. A or early Ausf. B with supplemental armor and a stowage box on the right fender. The large stowage bin (Gepäkkasten) on the right fender was introduced in May 1941. On the engine cover is a rack holding five Jerrycans. The third vehicle in line is a Pz.Kpfw. II (Flamm) flamethrower vehicle belonging to Pz.Abt. (F) 100. (Hans-Heiri Stapfer)

A column of tanks of Panzer-Abteilung (F) 101, a flamethrower battalion, is on the advance on the Eastern Front in 1941. In the foreground is a Pz.Kpfw. II, a late Ausf. B or Ausf. C with the characteristic cocentric circle markings of Pz.Abt 101. Both this tank and the next one in line have a smoke-grenade rack on the muffler shield, as well as a tilted rack with three smoke-grenade launchers on the fender next to the turret. (NARA)

An assemblage of Wehrmacht tanks in a village in the Soviet Union in the early part of the campaign on the Eastern Front includes a column of three up-armored, early-model Pz.Kpfw. IIs to the left. The vehicle at the front is has the cupola and right-side storage box modifications. Note the low, trapezoidal splash guard in front of the cupola. Interestingly, a divisional sign on the driver's frontal plate has either been censored on the photo, or eradicated on the tank itself. (NARA)

A column of vehicles of the 7th Panzer Division includes an up-armored, cupola-equipped Pz.Kpfw. II at the front. The left driver's vision port has two bolts below the vision slit, indicative of a late Ausf. B or an Ausf. C vehicle. The Y-shaped divisional sign is marked on the driver's frontal armor and to the rear of the Balkenkreuz on the side of the hull. What appears to be a wooden beam is secured to the right side of the hull. (NARA)

Churning up dust, a Pz.Kpfw. Ausf. A, B, or C of the 8th Panzer Division proceeds along a road in the Soviet Union. The turret has the cupola modification. Very faintly visible to the front of the side visor of the turret is the divisional sign: a yellow Y with a vertical yellow bar to the right of it. Next to the antenna trough and on the rear of the vehicle are rhomboidal plates with the vehicle number, 345. A smoke-grenade rack is on the muffler shield. (NARA)

Two Pz.Kpfw. IIs of the 13th Panzer Division negotiate a roadside ditch during the war in the Soviet Union. The closer tank bears vehicle number 805; note the vertically stored spare bogie wheel on the rear deck. The divisional sign is to the rear of the Balkenkreuz on the side of the hull: a circle with a cross in it. The farther vehicle is marked as a 2nd Battalion's staff vehicle number 14. Both tanks have the supplemental armor and the cupola modifications. (NARA)

Left: An armored column in the Soviet Union viewed from an open-topped car includes several Pz.Kpfw. IIs. The closest vehicle, an early-type Pz.Kpfw. II, has a grenade case leaning against the rear of the turret, and an N.K.A.V. smoke-grenade rack is dangling from the muffler shield. (NARA) **Right:** Markings for a 2nd Battalion staff vehicle are on the side of the turret of a Pz.Kpfw. II. The object on the front of the Gepäkkasten stowage box seems to be a section of spare track links. To the front of it is a spare bogie wheel. (NARA)

A Pz.Kpfw. II Ausf. A or early Ausf. B accompanies a Pz.Kpfw. IV Ausf. F across a steppe. The sign of the 9th Panzer Division is marked in yellow to the rear of the driver's left vision port: a Y with two vertical bars to the right of it. On the turret are markings for the number 11 staff vehicle of the 2nd Battalion. Note the crumpled fender and missing antenna trough. (NARA)

An up-armored, cupola-equipped Pz.Kpfw. II is on the advance in Russia. Markings for the 3rd Panzer Division are on the hull to the rear of the Balkenkreuz. The turret is marked for the number 6 staff vehicle of a 1st Battalion. The name "Franz Lott" is painted below the vehicle number. Jerrycans are stored vertically and horizontally on the rear deck. (NARA)

On this Pz.Kpfw. II with a cupola, supplemental armor, and turret side-rear visor in the style of an Ausf. A or early Ausf. B vehicle, Jerrycans are strapped to a rack above the fender. The vehicle number, 101, is marked on the turret in a color darker—probably yellow—than the Balkenkreuz on the hull. The side of a smoke-grenade rack is visible over the muffler. (NARA)

This up-armored, cupola-equipped Pz.Kpfw. II of the 3rd Panzer Division, which is driving onto an engineer bridge, has several atypical modifications, including a blank right driver's vision port and a prominent grab handle welded to the driver's door. The turret has markings for vehicle number 7 of the staff of the 2nd Battalion. (NARA)

A column of three Pz.Kpfw. IIs to the right of center is part of an armored advance in Russia. These three tanks are in the Ausf. A to C range and are marked with vehicle numbers, from front to rear, 41, 42, and 43. The letter K on the box on the rear of the Panzerbefehlswagen in the right background indicates Panzergruppe Kleist. (NARA)

Two tanks, including an up-armored Pz.Kpfw. II Ausf. A or early Ausf B in the foreground, advance along a trail in a forest. Both tanks are marked with the letter G on the frontal plates of the lower hulls, indicating Panzergruppe Guderian. (NARA)

An up-armored, cupola-equipped Pz.Kpfw. II Ausf. B passes a burning Soviet BT-7 tank. A very faint insignia to the immediate front of the vehicle number, 704, on the turret appears to be that of the 18th Panzer Division. Note the two vertically stored spare bogie wheels on or adjacent to the rear of the fender. (NARA)

The commander of a Pz.Kpfw. II Ausf. A, B, or C searches the ground to the right for signs of enemy movement. To his rear is a pedestal-mounted MG 34 for antiaircraft protection. The pedestal could be inserted in one of several sockets on the cupola; one of them is visible on the right edge of the cupola. To the left is a Pz.Kpfw. II Ausf. D (Flamm) flamethrower tank. (NARA)

A crewman of a 7th Panzer Division Pz.Kpfw. II is scanning through binoculars for evidence of the enemy near Demidov, Russia, on 20 July 1941. The Gepäkkasten normally installed as a modification on the right side of the hull is mounted on the left fender rear. Jerrycans are strapped to a wooden rack on the rear deck. On the hull above the antenna trough is the Y insignia of the 7th Panzer Division. (NARA)

A crewman from a Pz.Kpfw. II deals with Soviet prisoners of war. The number 375 on the side of the turret has been painted over an old, faded-out number; a 0 is visible under the number 7, and other traces of old numbers are under the 3 and the 5. Note the fabric blackout cover over the service headlight next to the Notek blackout headlight. The pad on the interior of the commander's hatch is seen to good advantage here. (NARA)

A knocked-out Pz.Kpfw. II of the 17th Panzer Division photographed on 14 July 1941 bears the letter G signifying Panzergruppe Guderian on the storage box. The explosion when the vehicle was hit blew the turret off. The cupola had sockets for an antiaircraft machine-gun mount. (NARA)

Three concentric circles on the rear corners of the turret was an identification scheme employed by Panzer-Abteilung (F) 101, a flamethrower battalion. The style of the vision ports was that of the Pz.Kpfw. II late Ausf. B and Ausf. C. A rack with three smoke-grenade launchers is on the fender to the rear of the turret. Below the 20mm cannon barrel, hidden in the trees in the background, is another Pz.Kpfw. II in the Ausf. A to C range. (NARA)

Left: A Soviet T-26 tank is burning to the front of a Pz.Kpfw. II of the 13th Panzer Division; the divisional symbol is on the rear plate of the radioman's compartment. Barely visible on the right and rear turret vision ports are the three-bolt configuration characteristic of Ausf. A and early Ausf. B vehicles. Markings for the 12th vehicle of the staff of 2nd Battalion are on the turret. Three spare track links are lying on the rear deck to the front of the smoke-grenade rack. (NARA) **Right:** The ruins of buildings form a stark backdrop for this Pz.Kpfw. II attached to Panzer-Abteilung z.b.V. 40 in Finland in 1941. Although difficult to discern, a piece of twisted wire holds together the inboard upper corners of the track sections to the left and the right of the driver's forward vision port. This closer than normal photo provides a good look at many of the small details on the front of the tank. (SA-kuva)

During Operation Barbarossa, the German invasion of the Soviet Union in 1941, the Germans deployed four divisions to Finland, on Russia's northern flank. Five days after the kickoff of the invasion, these crewmen are performing a barrel change on the 20mm gun of an up-armored Pz.Kpfw. II Ausf. A or B in Finland on 27 June. They were attached to Panzer-Abteilung z.b.V. 40. (The abbreviation z.b.V. stood for zur besonderen *Verwendung*: for special utilization.) The turret is retrofitted with a cupola. (SA-kuva)

Pz.Kpfw. IIs of Panzer-Abteilung z.b.V. 40 are parked in a settlement in Finland on 17 July 1941. All of the Pz.Kpfw. IIs are equipped with cupolas, and the turret of the vehicle in the right foreground has a rear vision port consistent with an Ausf. B or C vehicle. A stowage rack has been installed on the right fender. (SA-kuva)

A Pz.Kpfw. II with supplemental armor and a cupola, part of Panzer-Abteilung z.b.V 40, crosses a pontoon bridge in Finland. Spare track sections are on the left and right sides of the driver's frontal armor, covering his right and left vision ports, and more track sections are on the glacis. (SA-kuva)

A Pz.Kpfw. II of Panzer-Abteilung z.b.V. 40 is crossing a pontoon bridge on 21 August 1941 while another Pz.Kpfw. II in the foreground approaches the bridge. Cut sticks and several crates are stored on the rear of the closer vehicle, and a smoke-grenade rack is installed over the muffler. The vision ports on the rear and the right side of the turret are the type found on Ausf. B and C vehicles, with two bolts above and two bolts below the port, and two bolts below the vision slit on the port. (SA-kuva)

Two soldiers look over the wreckage of a Pz.Kpfw. II of Panzer-Abteilung z.b.V 40 that was knocked out, vehicle number 312. A close view of the stowage rack on the right fender reveals that a series of tie-down loops was affixed to its top edge. The driver's right vision port is unusual in that it has two bolts above the vision slit; the normal configuration of bolts for these hatches on vehicles with supplemental armor were either two bolts above the slit and one below it, or two bolts below the slit. (SA-kuva)

Photographed in August 1941, this Pz.Kpfw. II Ausf. A, B, or C of Panzer-Abteilung z.b.V. 40 appears to have taken a direct, penetrating hit on the mantlet on or just below the gunner's left vision port. The front fuel-filler cover is dangling on the top edge of the hull by the turret. On the ground to the far right is one of the supplemental armor plates for the driver's glacis. Note the bolt pattern on the right-hand side driver's viewport. There were several variations for this cover. (SA-kuva)

The vehicle number 300 is marked in worn paint on the rear of the turret of a Pz.Kpfw. II Ausf. A or B attached to Panzer-Abteilung z.b.V. 40. The muffler is missing its perforated shield. Faintly visible below the tailpipe is a Notek blackout taillight, also referred to as a convoy taillight. (SA-kuva)

A Panzer-Abteilung z.b.V. 40 Pz.Kpfw. II makes its way along a rough road in a forest in Finland. A helmet is hanging from the hook on the rear of the turret. An interesting detail on the rear of the Pz.Kpfw. II is the cutouts in the muffler shield and the two metal strips with a hole on each end, below the muffler shield, for mounting a smoke-grenade rack. (SA-kuva)

In Italy in the autumn of 1943, troops stand by as a Pz.Kpfw. II passes a Tiger tank along a road in Italy. The heap of branches on the Pz.Kpfw. II precludes a precise identification of the type. The rear idler suggests an Ausf. F, but an Ausf A–C has been seen with this feature too. The spare-track holder on the bow was instituted in January 1942. A Bosch headlight is visible through the branches. (NARA)

A Pz.Kpfw. II is parked along a road with a first-series Sturmpanzer IV to the rear of it in Italy. This closer look reveals that it is most likely an Ausf. B or C. The tank has various modifications, including supplemental armor, a Bosch headlight, a cupola, a spare-track holder on the bow, and a storage box on the right fender. A very close examination of the photograph reveals the characteristic bulge of an Ausf. F-type idler wheel. (NARA)

Pz.Kpfw. II Ausf. D

The next model of Pz.Kpfw. II after the Ausf. C was the Ausf. D, which featured an entirely new hull with thicker frontal armor (30mm as opposed to 14.5mm on the Ausf. C); new torsion-bar suspension; and redesigned bogie wheels, sprockets, and idlers. The turret retained the same basic design as the earlier Pz.Kpfw. IIs. The radio operator was moved to the right of the driver, and they shared a common, straight-across frontal plate with separate visors. Tank transporters are hauling six Pz.Kpfw. II Ausf. Ds past Hitler's reviewing stand during a military parade in Berlin. No markings are visible on these tanks. The turrets featured split hatches. (Thomas Anderson)

A mix of tank types including Pz.Kpfw. Is and Pz.Kpfw. IIs are being transported in a major military parade on 2 June 1939, probably the same one depicted in the preceding photograph. The nearest tank is a Pz.Kpfw. II Ausf. D, and another pair of Pz.Kpfw. II Ausf. D are on trailers in the next row of vehicles forward. The Ausf. D carried the same Maybach HL 62 TRM as the c, A-C versions, but had a top speed of 55km/h. (Hans-Heiri Stapfer)

The crew of a Pz.Kpfw. II Ausf. D enjoy the chilly winter weather. A total of 43 of these vehicles were completed, accepted, and issued to Panzer units. They saw service in Poland in 1939 with the Pz.Abt.(verl.) 66 of the 2nd and Pz.Abt.(verl.) 67 of the 3rd Light Divisions. (Thomas Anderson)

Panzer crewmen pose for their photograph next to a Pz.Kpfw. II Ausf. D. On the side of the upper hull is a rotating mount for the antenna. The protective trough for the antenna when lowered is mounted on the fender. Cooling louvers are present on the hull to the rear of the turret. Note the projection on the upper hull below the side of the turret. (Thomas Anderson)

In this August 1939 photo of a vehicle park consisting of transport vehicles and Pz.Kpfw. Is and IIs, all of the tanks have the fronts of their turrets—or hulls, in the case of the Pz.Kpfw. Is—marked with large identification crosses: a practice that saw widespread use in the 1939 invasion of Poland. In the left column, the first two vehicles are Pz.Kpfw. II Ausf. Ds. (Hans-Heiri Stapfer)

Two Pz.Kpfw. II Ausf. Ds, center and right, are moving out of a Panzer assembly area in Poland. In the background are several 38(t) tanks. (Thomas Anderson)

A column of tanks assume positions to engage targets to the left of the road. The second vehicle has the distinctive bogie wheels, hull projection below the turret, and side louvers of a Pz.Kpfw. II Ausf. D. In the foreground is a Pz.Kpfw. I Ausf. A. After the Polish Campaign, troops were ordered to turn in their Ausf. D vehicles, which were converted to flamethrower tanks. (NARA)

Pz.Kpfw. II (F) Ausf. A & B

The Waffenamt (Ordnance Department) proceeded with a program in 1939 to convert a number of Pz.Kpfw. II Ausf. D chassis to flamethrower tanks. Designated the Pz.Kpfw. II (Flamm), these vehicles featured a flamethrower in a small turret on each fender and a small non-rotating turret with a ball-mounted MG 34 with visors to each side. Fuel was stored inside the vehicle, and an armored box on each fender held two tanks of compressed-nitrogen propellant. Shown here is a Pz.Kpfw. II (Flamm) Ausf. B, distinguished by the eight-spoked sprocket and lubricated-pin tracks. The Ausf. A had 11-spoked sprockets to accommodate the dry-pin tracks of that vehicle. (NARA)

On the center of the Pz.Kpfw. II (Flamm) glacis, between the service headlights, was a Notek blackout headlight. Also on the glacis were two doors for the driver and the radio operator. These flamethrowers are equipped with extensions on the nozzles; this is particularly apparent on the flamethrower on the right fender. Above the driver's and radio operator's visors is a rain shield, added during production of these vehicles. (NARA)

Following the initial experience of flamethrower crews with the Pz.Kpfw. II (Flamm), the original front track guards were replaced with curved ones with raised edges to form troughs, to divert the flame fuel to the fronts of the tracks. The turret had a single, front-hinged hatch door with a periscope guard on top of it. (NARA)

A group of Kradschützen pass an Pz.Kpfw. II (Flamm) that is waylaid on the side of a road. The vehicle appears to have sustained mine damage to the fourth roadwheel on the left side. This damage has also dislodged the left side track. The flamethrowers have recently seen considerable use, as evidenced by the heavy flame fuel staining on the front left fender. This staining has also extended to the front of the hull. (NARA)

Vehicle number 213 is marked on the rear of this Pz.Kpfw. II (Flamm) assigned to the 2nd Company, Panzer-Abteilung (F) 101. The concentric-circle identification sign of this battalion is visible on the left corner of the turret. A blackout taillight, or convoy taillight, is above the tailpipe. (NARA)

A Pz.Kpfw. II (Flamm) of the 3rd Company, Panzer-Abteilung (F) 100 is driving onto an engineer bridge. Five Jerrycans are stored on the rear deck, and canvas dust covers have been fitted over the flamethrowers. (NARA)

A Pz.Kpfw II Ausf. F speeds past soldiers taking a break along a highway in North Africa. A fair amount of equipment and baggage is stored on the rear deck and the fenders. Markings in black are present on the side and the rear of the turret but are illegible. The Ausf. F was an extensive redesign of the tank. Note the different muffler on the right side of the rear plate. (Image Bank WW2)

A truck full of Italian troops passes a Pz.Kpfw. II Ausf. F of the 5th Panzer Regiment, 21st Panzer Division in North Africa. The Ausf. F has a different idler wheel than earlier Panzer IIs, although it has been seen retrofitted to earlier production tanks. A wooden storage box has been mounted on the rear of the turret. On the upper hull, below the number 2 on the turret, the chassis number of this tank has been marked in white, but the number is illegible. (NARA)

The British captured this Pz.Kpfw. II Ausf. F of the Headquarters Reconnaissance Platoon, 7th Panzer Regiment, 10th Panzer Division, in Tunisia in May 1943. The tank was built in May 1942 and arrived in Tunisia in December of that year. The vehicle is currently on display at The Tank Museum, Bovington. The storage box has since been repaired, but the crumpled fender remains in the state seen here to this day. Note the bison insignia of the 7th Panzer Regiment on the left rear of the turret, formed by spraying a dark color around a stencil of the animal. A spare wheel sits on top of the armored smoke grenade dispenser. (Patton Museum)

Markings for a regimental staff vehicle number 06 are on the sides and rear of the captured Pz.Kpfw. II Ausf. F of the 7th Panzer Regiment. The letter R was applied somewhat carelessly, with its top leaning to the right. This vehicle was Fahrgestell (chassis) number 28434, produced by the Ursus factory in Warsaw, Poland. (Patton Museum)

The Panzer II Ausf. F featured a single, flat front plate that was 30mm thick over the driver's station, with a dummy visor on the right-hand side. The curved bow that was covered with supplemental armor on earlier models was changed to sections of flat plate. Sections of armor have been cut out of this Pz.Kpfw. II Ausf. F, permitting a view of some of the internal components. In the turret, the interior of the rear vision port and the underside of the cupola assembly are visible. Below, in the hull, the radio operator's vision port and the operating mechanism for lowering and raising the radio antenna are in view. The cast-armor vision ports on the mantlet are raised. (APG)

A Pz.Kpfw. II Ausf F followed by two motorcycles with sidecars crosses an engineer bridge over a creek somewhere in the Soviet Union in June 1942. A white number 175 is painted on the turret between the vision ports, and a white and black Balkenkreuz is faintly visible through the glare on the storage box on the fender. (BA 216-0412-16)

During the encirclement of Smolensk during Operation Barbarossa in 1941, Pz.Kpfw. IIs accompany infantrymen as they advance. In the foreground is a Pz.Kpfw. II Ausf. F with baggage piled high on the rear deck and crew helmets hanging from the sides of the turret. A new three-point tow cable holder was fitted to the Ausf. F on the right glacis. Sometimes a spare wheel holder has mounted atop it. (NARA).

A Pz.Kpfw. II Ausf. F in the foreground follows two Sd.Kfz. 251s and, farther forward, several more armored vehicles, including another Pz.Kpfw. II Ausf. F, during an advance across a steppe on the Eastern Front. The Pz.Kpfw. II Ausf. F in the foreground has an irregular camouflage pattern painted on it, including on the muffler shield. The number 367 is painted in white on the side and the rear of the turret. The Ausf. F featured a new hatch for the radio operator and a redesigned radiator access hatch but these are hard to discern from period photos as they are often covered with stowage. (NARA)

A Pz.Kpfw. II Ausf. F has paused next to a radio truck during the advance of the Grossdeutschland Division in the Soviet Union in the summer of 1942. Tree branches are arranged on the vehicle for camouflage. A map case and a canteen hang from the hook on the rear of the turret. On top of the toolbox on the rear of the right fender is a carrying case for hand grenades. (NARA)

The commander of a Pz.Kpfw. II Ausf. F of the Grossdeutschland Division watches a Fieseler Storch liaison and observation plane fly past in the Soviet Union in 1942. Clear details are visible of the driver's visor and the dummy visor next to it, as well as the three brackets for holding a tow cable on the right side of the glacis. The cupola of this vehicle was fitted with sockets for mounting an antiaircraft machine gun. (NARA)

Left: Another tank in the same column seen in the previous photo, the Pz.Kpfw. II Ausf. F in the foreground is part of a column making its way around a pond. On the rear of the turret is a marking with three horizontal bars with the number 3 to the right of them; the tilted white object over these markings is a small, illegible sign hanging from the hook behind the cupola. Spare track links, a spare road wheel, and a Jerry can are stored on the left side of the rear deck. **Right:** A good view of the large stowage box, or Gepäckkasten, that was a feature of the Pz.Kpfw. II Ausf. F—but also retrofitted to early models of the Pz.Kpfw. II—is available in this photo. The square recess on the bottom of the side of the box was to provide clearance for the fender support, the angle iron visible in the recess. The two lids on the top of the box were secured with the thin rod with a loop on the front end and the padlock on the rear. This rod passed through loops on the side of the box, thus holding the two hasps on each lid. Very faintly visible on the side of the box are two faded markings: a heart-shaped insignia at the front and a black and white Balkenkreuz at the center. (NARA, both)

This Pz.Kpfw. II Ausf. F has an interesting arrangement of a long section of track mounted around the turret. The means of supporting the track in such a straight manner is not clear, but a wire is visible from the hook on the rear of the turret to the track. (NARA)

Left: A crewman of a Pz.Kpfw. II Ausf. F washes himself from a bucket next to his vehicle. A small metal box is strapped to the side of the hull next to the dummy visor, covering the right vision port. A tarpaulin has been draped over the top of the turret. **Right:** During the winter somewhere on the Eastern Front, a Pz.Kpfw. II Ausf. F precedes a couple of horse-drawn supply wagons. Evidence of deteriorating whitewash is apparent on the tank. The driver's visor is in the fully open position, with the vision slot visible and the holes for the binocular periscope hidden by the visor. Helmets are hanging on the sides of the turret. (TAG, both)

The driver's front visor signifying a Pz.Kpfw. II Ausf. F is faintly visible on this vehicle with winter whitewash camouflage, poised to cover the flank of a road running through a settlement on the Eastern Front. The number 23 is discernable on the turret, and the dark object to the front of the digits is a helmet. (TAG)

Two Pz.Kpfw. II Ausf. F tanks are crossing a pontoon bridge over an icy river. The lead vehicle is marked 956 on the turret. On the bank in the background is a half-track with a quadruple 20mm gun mount, positioned to defend the bridgehead against air attack. (NARA)

During a pause in the advance of SS-Panzergrenadier Division "Leibstandarte Adolf Hitler" on the outskirts of Kharkov, Ukraine, in March 1943, the radio operator of the second vehicle, a Pz.Kpfw. II Ausf. F, casually reads a newspaper while the commander of the vehicle stands in the cupola, looking to the rear. On the armored cover for the smoke-grenade rack to the left of the muffler are a black-and-white Balkenkreuz and the divisional insignia. These vehicles are all whitewashed for winter camouflage. (BA 067-14)

Pz.Kpfw. II Ausf. G

Following the Pz.Kpfw. II Ausf. F series, a new and faster version of the Pz.Kpfw. II was planned. This took shape as the VK 901, which also went under several other designations, including the Pz.Kpfw. II Ausf. G. The key features of the vehicle were its speed, a maximum of 65 km/h, and its stabilized weapons mount, permitting the 20mm KwK 38 cannon and 7.92mm MG 34 to be fired accurately while the tank was moving. (Akira Takiguchi)

A group of older officers armed with a variety of weapons is on a Pz.Kpfw. II Ausf. G. They are members of an anti-partisan unit in Grodek, Poland. On the left side of the hull near the rear corner are tactical markings for an armored car company and a corps headquarters. This vehicle had five pairs of interleaved bogie wheels on each side. It was powered by a 150 horsepower Maybach HL 45 engine through a VG 15319 transmission. (Akira Takiguchi)

In 1941 two pilot light tank destroyers were constructed using VK 901 (i.e., Pz.Kpfw. II Ausf. G) chassis, with a 50mm Pak 38 antitank gun mounted in an open-topped superstructure. The vehicle, designated the Pz.Sfl. Ic (Panzer Selbstfahrlafette: armored self-propelled carriage), was to have a four-man crew, with 30mm frontal armor and 20mm side armor. Plans to mass-produce the Pz.Sfl. Ic were abandoned, and the two pilots were serving with Panzerjäger-Abteilung (Sfl.) 559 on the Eastern Front in August 1942. (Patton Museum)

Pz.Kpfw. II Ausf. J

The Pz.Kpfw. II Ausf. J was also known as the VK1601. Thirty examples were produced. The design was intended to increase armor protection without increasing weight and featured 80mm armor plate on the frontal surfaces and 50mm on the sides and rear. It was armed with a 20mm KwK 38 cannon and a 7.92mm MG 34. A distinguishing feature was the interrupted fender on each side to allow clearance for a circular hatch on the hull. The photo on this page shows a VK 1601 Versuchs-Fahrgestell (experimental chassis), similar to the production VK 1601 chassis, undergoing weight tests with a large concrete slab on top, at the MAN factory in Nürnberg. This chassis lacks the front visors of the production chassis, and has a different design of splash guard over the driver's and radio operator's compartments. (Thomas Anderson)

A Pz.Kpfw. II Ausf. J and what appears to be another tank of that type both are carrying local camouflage in the form of tree branches. Five VK1601 were issued to 1Kp./Pz.Abt.z.b.V.66 in May 1942 with tropical camouflage, as they were intended for Operation Herkules—the invasion of Malta. They were instead sent to 12th Panzer Division and used around Leningrad. (Thomas Anderson)

Wehrmacht troops pose for their photo on a Pz.Kpfw. II Ausf. J. Holes for tow shackles were on extensions on the front ends of the side armor of the hull. Like the Luchs, the Pz.Kpfw. II Ausf. J had a short track-to-ground contact length, at about 71 inches. The tracks were the dry-pin Kgs 61-500/160. (Thomas Anderson)

A Pz.Kpfw. II Ausf. J is participating in a winter exercise. The driver and, on his right, the radio operator each had a side vision port mounted on a round plate that was bolted to the hull. The object casting a shadow on the side of the hull toward the rear is the basket of a ski pole. (Thomas Anderson)

Two Pz.Kpfw. II Ausf. Js of the *13. verstärkte Polizei-Panzer-Kompanie* share the right of way with a farmer and his milk cow. *"Verstaerkte,"* in this case means reinforced—the unit also includes Panzer IVs. The tanks are apparently painted in the scheme of *Dunkelgrau* (dark gray), and the only visible markings on the second vehicle are white identification crosses on the side hatches and the smoke-grenade rack cover on the rear. Tow cables and two spare track-links are on the rear of that vehicle. There are a trio of Steyr ADGZ armored cars near the front of the column. (Thomas Anderson)

Pz.Kpfw. II "Luchs"

The vehicle popularly known as the Luchs (Lynx), or more formally as the VK 1303, the Pz.Kpfw. II Ausf. L, and a succession of other designations, was conceived as a fully-tracked armored reconnaissance vehicle. It had the same lower hull and suspension as the Pz.Kpfw. II Ausf. G but solid wheels and a wider upper hull to accommodate a larger turret ring. The vehicle was armed with a 20mm KwK 38 L/55 cannon and a 7.92mm MG 34 machine gun. This example, chassis umber 200164 and turret number 200143, was produced by MAN in the summer of 1943 and captured by the British during the war. It is now preserved at The Tank Museum, Bovington. (Patton Museum)

Luchs chassis number 200164 is viewed from the right rear in a photograph taken after its capture by the British. The muffler and tailpipe were missing, the right fender was severely damaged, and various accessories had been removed. A Jerrycan is still on the rack on the right side of the turret. The turret had a rear entry door; the one shown here is the late-type wide model. The Luchs was powered by a 180 horsepower Maybach HL 66 P and top speed was an impressive 60 Km/h. (Patton Museum)

The Luchs was equipped with Kgs 63/360/90 tracks, which were 14.17 inches wide, with a pitch of 3.54 inches. A section of spare track was in a holder on the bow. The driver had a visor, above which were two openings for a binocular periscope. The turret had only one vision port, on the right side. For viewing the outside from other angles, the commander and the gunner relied on two periscopes. On the mantlet to the left of the 20mm cannon was the aperture for the MG 34. To the right of the 20mm gun was a small aperture for the gunner's telescopic sight. (Patton Museum)

In a view through the rear door of the turret of a Luchs, at the center is the 20mm gun and mount. To the left is the mount for the 7.92mm MG 34. To the right are the traversing gear and hand wheel as well as the mount for the gunner's Turmzielfernrohr 6 articulated telescope. In the hull to the lower front are the driver's compartment, left, and the radio operator's compartment, right. (Patton Museum)

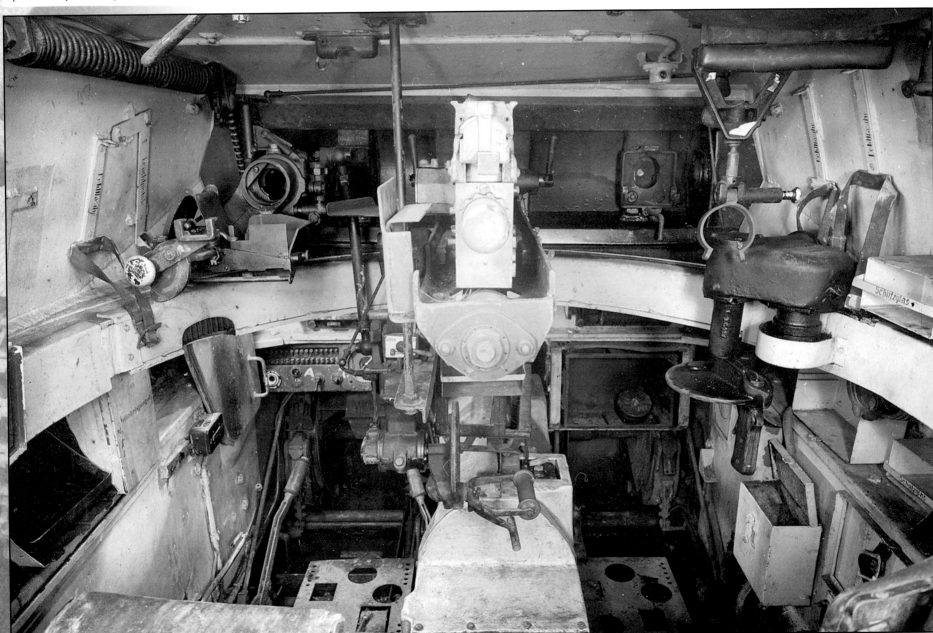